Vivia

The Legend of Vivia Thomas:

A Novelette in Poems

Vivia

The Legend of Vivia Thomas:

A Novelette in Poems

by

Linda Neal Reising

Cover design by Shay Culligan
Cover art by Catrin Welz-Stein
Author photo by Emma Carner

ISBN: 978-1-63980-369-9

Kelsay Books
502 South 1040 East, A-119
American Fork, Utah 84003
Kelsaybooks.com

This book is dedicated to the memory
of my father, Leroy Neal—
lifetime Oklahoman, family man, veteran,
musician, singer, and storyteller extraordinaire.

A special thank you to Jessica Thompson
and Mark Williams who were the first to read
these words and are always first to encourage me.

Contents

Part II

Part III

Prologue

There is no doubt that Vivia Thomas was a real person, that she lived, died, and was buried at the Fort Gibson National Cemetery in Fort Gibson, Oklahoma, in 1870. Almost everything else about the woman's life is a question mark, surrounded by mystery and conjecture. In fact, her story is not one of biography, but of legend. When I first read about Vivia's fascinating life, or at least the stories that have been created about her, I knew that I wanted to learn more, and if that proved impossible, then to create my own tales about her, to make her a living, breathing person.

The online postings of Wade Burleson and Marilyn A. Hudson have been invaluable in "putting together" Vivia's story. However, all of the poems about her early life which I have included in this book are completely imaginary, created by researching the time and place in which Vivia lived. After all, are we not all products of the era in which we live, the location where our roots are planted?

Just like Vivia, we will all live, die, and fade into obscurity. Unless, of course, we become legends, having our stories told around campfires. And, who knows, maybe we will linger nearby, listening.

*I never meant to become a legend . . . but then again
there were so many things I never meant to become.*

Part I

My Birth (1840)

My grandmother once told me when my mother
was not near—for such matters were not discussed
among ladies—that I was born without breath,
blue as the moon on the Boston snow that night
in January, when I made my entrance into this world.
The doctor, a friend of my father's, would have
declared me dead had it not been for the quick action
of an Irish girl, hired as a wet nurse only the day
before, after her child had succumbed to a fever
at two weeks of age. Aideen was her name, and she
took my limp body in her rough hands, chafed
my chest. Then, according to Grandmother, she put
her mouth to my lips, breathed her own life into mine,
saying a Hail Mary every time she raised her head
to draw a breath. My family was not Catholic,
and her words surely sounded like a spell, an incantation,
as she called to her Holy Mother, desperate to save
this baby, a baby not of her womb. Her magic worked,
and I gasped air, screamed my way into this life.
Perhaps, as I look back now, it would have been better
if the peasant girl had wrapped me in the soft shawl
my mother had knitted, had hurried from the house
to bury me beside her little one, maybe making
a bargain with her gods, an exchange of one child
for another, a soul for a soul, one much worthier
than mine.

Aideen

My mother did not recover from my birth
for some time, having just delivered my brother
only a year earlier. There had been three girls
and two small, white crosses in the graveyard
before the birth of Charles, so he was greeted
with great jubilation, named after our father.
My brother carried sunshine on his shoulders,
and years later, when I saw drawings of Atlas
in my schoolbooks, the god bearing the world,
I thought that it looked like Charles if the orb
had been glowing and warm. So, I was left
to Aideen. Is it possible to possess a memory
from such an early age? There are times
I seem to capture a moment from long ago,
being cradled in her warm arms, my face pressed
against her soft breast, everything soft
as I twirl a red curl that falls softly down
her shoulder, and listen as she sings
a soft song whose words I do not know
but which always brings a soft tear
that drops onto my upturned, adoring face.

Early Childhood

My sisters—Ann, Margaret, Julia—doted
on me at first, a live doll to dress and adorn
with ribbons and lace. But once I walked,
talked enough to say *no,* I was a nuisance
to them, sisters born so close together,
they now moved as one into the in-between
time, when childhood begins to turn gray, to lose
the color of wonder, and womanhood beckons.
One day they were calling and chirping to one
another amid the wing flap of taffeta, the next,
they were simply gone, the house still and silent
as a world muffled in cotton batting. My father
had insisted that they all go away to school,
to learn to become the kind of ladies that men—
men of a certain rank in society—would wish
to marry. I was left alone with Aideen and Charles,
who could not play every day. He was whisked
away by my father to learn how to shake hands,
to look an opponent in the eye, to become
one of those men of a certain rank in society.

Alone

When Aideen and I were alone, she dressed
me in my best coat, forest green in color,
with a collar of red fox fur, and we ventured
into a world of noise and smells, a society
I would never have known existed, protected
as I was, like a daguerreotype behind glass.
We walked away from the granite-stoned
streets outside my home to clustered shops,
where women haggled over the cost of cabbage.
She held my small, gloved hand, shoved
her way through crowds of people, disheveled
in their destitution, desperate from deprivation.
But not one ever made a move to harm me
as Aideen navigated us through the seas
of humanity. And no matter our errands,
we always ended at a cemetery, devoid
of tombstones and monuments like the ones
in the graveyard behind our church. Markers
were nothing more than flat stones stood
upright, blank and moss-covered, or twigs,
bound together with twine, leather. Kneeling,
she whispered a prayer to clutched beads,
while I stood in silence, wishing she loved me
as much as the bone child beneath the ground.

Torn Away

How strange the passage of time when one
is a child—long, languorous days of summer,
sun-silken and warm, dappling through elms.
Hours crawl like common garden snails, content
to inch from peony stalk to dahlia stem. Drowsy
dreams fill the daylight like a sated bee dozing
inside a blossom. I remember thinking my blessed
life would always be like this. Even my mother, cold
in her affections most of the time, would stroke
my hair as I lay my head on her lap, as we lounged
on a wicker settee under an arbor of wisteria.
Five summers passed in this way. One day,
as I plucked a rose for Aideen, she brought her hands
to her face and wept, great breathless sobs,
caught in her throat, and I asked if a thorn had pierced
her hand. She drew me to her, saying, no, her heart
was pierced instead. Our time together was coming
to an end. I was no longer a baby, in need of nurture,
but a child old enough to learn real lessons—reading,
writing—all of the wonders she had never known.
Within the week, a governess would be arriving to take
her place. I placed my face against her cheek and sent
up a howl that filled the August air, but nothing would ever
fill my own emptiness.

The Governess

Aideen left one night while I slept, tucked in slumber,
and I never saw her again. At first, when I walked
to church with my mother or tagged along, shopping
for my grandmother's special yarn or teas, I searched
the crowd for her sweet face, and more than once I spied
a woman with long red hair bustling toward a shop,
but she never stopped when I called her name. Charles
could not understand my weeping over someone Father
had taught him was a maid, nothing more, no more
important than the groom who mucked the stalls,
the old woman whose broom kept the streets clean
in front of our carriage steps so our skirts were left
unsoiled. I coiled myself into a ball of loneliness.
Charles had drawn his nourishment at our mother's
breast, felt the adoration of our father, but I had only
known Aideen. It was a fortnight before the governess
arrived, attired in her stern grey bodice and skirt,
the livery man trailing behind her holding a valise
and small chest tucked beneath his arm. My chest
tightened as she stood in the vestibule, husking
her gloves from long fingers. Her chestnut hair,
parted in the middle, was caught by combs in back,
while two curls spiraled a frame around her porcelain
face. She only met my eyes when Mother pushed me
forward, and I saw something I was not expecting—
an expression I had no word for then, but now would call
collusion.

Miss Janice

I learned on the very first day, alone with my teacher,
that *Janice* was indeed her last name, her first
being Louisa. She asked if I knew who Janus
was in mythology, and I confessed my ignorance,
as I would again and again over the next nine years.
Janus, she said, as she spread an array of paintbrushes
on the table, was a two-faced Roman god, looking
forward and backward all at the same time. Likewise,
she had learned as a governess to wear two faces—
one for the students and one for their parents, a trick
she had learned from her childhood governess. Once
from a family far wealthier than mine, her parents
had been lost at sea on a voyage to Europe, leaving
her to an uncle who squandered the family fortune.
She now possessed nothing more than her education,
her razor-sharp mind, and a steely determination
to make her own way, slapping away the hands
offered her in marriage, some by men deceived
into believing that Uncle was still a man of means
instead of a mean drunk who cheated at cards
and still managed to lose. Miss Janice opened
my innocent eyes, spoke with me, adult to adult,
though I was a small child, and I longed to be strong
like her. While Aideen taught me the strength
of love, Miss Janice taught me the love of strength.

Awakening

Miss Janice woke me from my unknowing,
first by teaching me letters that joined hands
to form words, which lined up like school
children to form sentences. She taught
me to sit with proper posture, to practice
my penmanship—convex curves, concave
curves, oblique straight lines, up-strokes,
down-strokes, and always the flourishing
of pen on paper, making art from the ordinary.
She unwrapped the riddle of numbers,
assuring me that women could cypher
as well as men, even though we should hold
that secret close. We talked about stars, the moon,
and ocean tides. Collected flowers and leaves
that I labeled and pressed inside book leaves.
French, piano, watercolors—I mastered all
of the feminine subjects that were expected
of young ladies in my day. But best of all
I loved history, reading of kings and queens
who wielded their power from thrones
not always meant for them, who dealt
with their enemies swiftly, no forethought,
no regret—an important lesson I failed to learn.

Freedom

On sunny days, my governess assured Mother
that we needed to retreat to the countryside
to strengthen my lungs and to practice landscape
sketches. Samuel, stable boy and protector,
would hitch a horse to the carriage, hand
us up onto the seat, a basket from the kitchen
between. I lived for those days, hours free
from rules that bound my spirit like a corset,
tied so tightly that I could not breathe at times.
We would lie prone, drawing Black-eyed
Susans and Purple Thistle, until Miss Janice
would stand, dust off her skirt, and assert
that the fun should begin. Samuel positioned
under his chin an old violin, given to him
by his father, who had died and left him
nothing more than the music that lived
inside his fingers. I did not know the songs
he sawed and sang, but my teacher took
my hands and we whirled, skirts swirling
around our legs that were never allowed
to know the light of day. We danced, dizzy
with delight, until we tumbled, laughing
more than I would ever laugh again,
but I was too young to know that or to care.

Arrangements

Nine years passed in a flurry of family
happenings—the daily tide of rising, dining,
sleeping—sprinkled with larger events—
weddings, deaths. Miss Janice and I continued
our secret life, although the joy I had once seen
in her eyes began to dim, like fog shawling a gas
street light. One evening, Father brought home
a friend dressed in a fine suit, a man just flirting
with middle age, gray already glinting amid
his bushy sideburns. After ceremonial cigars
and scotch, my father sent the maid to fetch
my teacher, and the heavy walnut doors
of his office were closed behind the three.
When she emerged, Miss Janice swept up
the stairs to her room and clicked the lock
in place. I had learned too many manners
to knock, so I knew nothing until morning
when she set aside our lessons for the day,
sat beside me, took my hand. She had made
a promise of marriage, she softly told me.
Mr. Owen, owner of mills, where women
worked themselves to deafness from roar
of machines weaving wool, was a widower
rearing two young sons. He could provide
security, while Miss Janice would provide
a respected family name, motherly love.
I begged her not to go, but she told me
our time together was over. I was leaving
for school. She would put on yet another
new face, always carry a veiled heart.

School Arrival

The last task Miss Janice performed was packing
my bags for Miss Porter's Finishing School, tucked
away in Connecticut, a place in the countryside
where fourteen-year-old girls could be formed
into good Christian wives and mothers, though young
enough to cry for their own. Miss Janice rode
beside me in the closed carriage, carried herself
like a wooden image of the person who had shared
my deepest dreams and doubts. We traveled
for three days, and when we arrived, she did not enter
the building, but pulled me close and whispered
to remember all she had taught me, to remember
to wear the face that others wanted to see, but keep
my truth tucked close to my heart. She slipped
into my hand a fragile chain with a forget-me-not
charm, then commanded the driver to depart,
leaving me, surrounded by my possessions, waiting
for someone to escort me through the doors
of my next life. This time, I did not cry with abandon
at what seemed like abandonment. I felt my tears
catch in my throat, turn solid, as if King Midas
had reached out a jeweled finger, transformed
me into a cold, gold statue.

Miss Porter's

The parlor was filled with girls pretending
to be ladies, each one coifed and corseted,
sitting primly with needlepoint upon laps,
chatting softly as their needles performed
ballet through cloth. Their skin was porcelain
pale, like fragile teacups, and I felt a flash
of shame for the days spent hatless, unveiled,
the summer sun soaking through my skirt
as I stretched out in a meadow or hitched
my slips high, mounted Jack, the horse
untethered from our carriage, and rode
him, bareback, the heat caught in his mane.
My poor mother purchased arsenic wafers,
meant to bleach my brown skin white again,
but I burned them in my fireplace, afraid
to poison myself for beauty. But I withstood
the baths of milk, the plasters of strawberries,
that did little to ease my mother's lament
that I looked like a farmhand, my hands
too rough to be held ungloved. Now I stood
before a whole room of bisque figurines.

A Friend

My time at school would have been a prison
sentence had it not been for Claire, a crow-haired
girl who took me under her wing, taught me rules
not always written but understood. Rules
about laughing and talking, mainly refraining
from both. Rules about following schedules,
each day planned out in regimental blocks.
Rules about being a genteel lady, blushing
and swooning on cue. Rules about following
rules. Claire and I lived for special Saturdays,
when we were allowed a few hours to walk
hand in hand through the village—a woman
should never be seen alone. We giggled
and chattered like blue jays as we window
shopped, bought sweets to share in the shade.
Sometimes a young man would raise his hat
to us, but we were trained to cast our eyes
down, to discourage familiarity, until alone
again, then we burst into laughter, teasing
each other about which should have him
as a husband. Out of all my memories,
these rank among the fondest. I called
those times *honey days*—so sweet, so golden.

Education

We spent our days at Miss Porter's practicing
elocution and oratory, reciting the works of Keats
and Bryant, Wordsworth and Tennyson. I threw
myself into "Charge of the Light Brigade," drawing
a reprimand for my enthusiasm about the manly
art of war and forced to recite "Perfect Woman,"
ending with the "angelic light" that all women
were expected to possess, but which somehow
God had failed to place within me. We chanted
phrases in Latin, French, German—preparing
for the Grand Tour with husbands yet to be met.
Even when we played "Graces," each girl tossing
to her partner a hoop from a stick, we worked
not at winning, but at moving gracefully, creating
a tableau of white-clad Greek goddesses frolicking.
History, fine arts, literature—topics we could use
to create conversation at a dinner party or ball—
were meant to make us seem more interesting
than we truly were. It was as if all the subjects
we studied were lures, traps, to capture a man
to care for us since we were not allowed to care
for ourselves. And always there was the endless
needlework, the embroidery of each day— hooping,
lock stitch, running stitch—hours spent on samplers
when I wanted nothing more than to sample life.

Eighteen

At eighteen, I graduated to adulthood, stepped
into a world that was changing as much as I.
There were rumblings, warnings of disaster
to come for our country, and I was reminded
of studying about the 1812 Missouri earthquake
that made the Mississippi River run backwards,
shook the earth so much that Boston's church bells
rang. Only this time, the divisions were in our
people, not in chasms that swallowed farmsteads.
Words of war floated on the air, but I tried to wipe
them from my mind. My time had come for coming
out, for buying all of the finery required to impress,
to be well-dressed, well-schooled in poise, charm.
We girls used to chant a little rhyme, *If not engaged
in three, then an old maid you shall be.* Season
one, I was sure, would be enough time for me
to find a man I could marry. Unlike most girls,
I did not dream of love but of someone free
in thought, full of adventure, a man willing
to let me lie in meadows watching shooting stars,
to ride a roan without a side saddle, to dance
an Irish jig to a fiddle tune. But I learned early
a lady must not let a man know such desires—
any desires.

Coming Out Debut

My mother had never cared to spend long hours
with me, preferring tea parties or a game of Whist
or a séance summoning the spirit of someone
departed, trying to part the curtain dividing
this life from the beyond. But now she beamed
as we entered the dressmaker's shop. Her hope
floating on the notion that she could transform
me into a vision, as lovely as my sisters
had been as they swept into ballrooms, swept
young men off their feet, procuring proposals
of marriage in their first seasons. Now, years
later, they spent their days running households
filled with servants and children, a domestic
diorama that left me numb with boredom.
But I tried to smile, wear my Janus face,
as the seamstress measured my waist,
brought forth seas of satin, chiffon, lace.
I sat silent as my mother made selections,
held up swatches to match my eyes,
eyes that could not see the pattern of my future
that she was determined to trace for me.

Cotillion

If I had been the kind of young woman who swooned,
I would have done so when I caught my reflection
in the pier mirror that graced our hall. My cotillion
dress was a cloud of purity—white chiffon over white
silk, a white velvet ribbon that crossed from shoulder
to waist, ending with a cluster of white heather.
I had seen paintings of Queen Victoria on her wedding
day, and my dress, although not a copy, borrowed
from it. I am sure my mother was hoping I would walk
down the aisle of our church in this dress in less
than a year. I felt like a stage actress in costume,
ready to deliver a soliloquy, but I had not learned
my lines. Once there, I sleep-walked into a room
filled with wax candles casting soft light on gliding
couples. Girls with blossom-wreathed heads swirled
in skirts of tulle, led by men in glazed shirt fronts
and fresh gloves. My dance card was quickly filled,
and I joined the parade of performers, for truly,
that is what we were, moving through the gestures
and steps we had practiced for weeks. At midnight,
we went to supper, but I could not swallow
more than a few bites, and soon I was twirling
on the dance floor once more. Etiquette
demanded that we not dance more than once
with the same partner, so the night was a zoetrope
of black tailcoats, polished shoes, white ties.

Silence

For days after the cotillion, my mother paced
the parqueted floors of our house, waiting
for calling cards to be brought to our door,
cards that never came. Was I less lovely,
less charming than the other girls thumbing
through a stack of gentlemen's names engraved
on fine linen paper? Was my family tainted
in any way—morally, financially? No, matters
of the heart are mysterious, and I never found
the clues, the key, required to unlock the riddle.
While my mother spent hours wringing her hands,
jumping at the ringing of our doorbell, I found
my breathing slowing back to normal, my spirits
soaring as if an iron weight had been lifted
from a feather. I knew how a man sentenced
to prison felt if he were granted a pardon,
set free to live his life. Until the next courting
season, I could remain unfettered, untied
to any man. Mother kept repeating, *You
will be left on the shelf,* and I had to agree—
but not like some rotting pear, attracting flies,
rather a delicate crystal vase, filled with daisies.

Seasons Two and Three

Each spring, as Mother, disheartened, dug through bolts
of fabric, searching for the perfect shade to cast
a net over a beau, I noticed that the colors she chose
grew darker. Season one had been white, virginal,
perfect for a trip down a lily-lined aisle. Second season,
she settled upon a pale sea foam green, but the tide
of courtship did not turn, the season ebbed, left me
stranded once again without a suitor for my hand.
For season three, she paid to have made a dress
so pink I blush to remember it. I turned twenty
that year, and I feared the color cried out silent
desperation, but I twirled the tulle around ballroom
floors, smiled, curtsied, played the coquette, filled
with regret only because I knew my mother
would be distraught once more, for no man
made an impression on me, nor I on him.
Remembering our girlhood chant—*If not engaged
in three, then an old maid you shall be*—I resigned
myself to playing the role of doting aunt, the kind
who sneaked sweets to nieces and nephews, planted
kisses on plump cheeks that they fiercely swiped clean.

A Different Kind of Season

I turned twenty-one four months before the fourth
season of my disgrace was to begin. Mother
was plotting, scheming ways to make me look
younger, prettier than the girls making first
appearances on the marital market stage.
But all of that was forgotten in April of '61
when guns were fired at Ft. Sumter. Three
days later, Massachusetts sent troops, first
in the Union. Young men abandoned escort
duties—holding out their arms to lead women
to dinner or a dance—picked up arms instead.
We could not know then how many years
would fill with wasted waiting, how many
brides would be widowed before bearing
a child, or worse, be left with fatherless
children to feed. As in all wars, each side
thought that God would send down victory
like a burning bush, choosing the righteous,
but I did not think that any war was heavenly,
it was only man willing to destroy with such wrath.

Volunteer

Charles had followed his namesake into business—
shipping and trade that had made Father wealthy
enough to stretch his long arms into the realms
of real estate and banking. Since only men
could pursue a profession, Charles took up the reins,
though if truth be told, I was the one with the mind
for figures. Numbers always spoke sense to me,
and many times, my brother sought my advice
on investments, but we did not share our secret.
Charles accepted the praise, but I felt the pride
inside. My brother had become the most eligible
young man in Boston, and young ladies strolled
along the walks outside our stately home, hoping
for a glance or chance encounter. But it was bells
of war and not of marriage that rang for Charles
that April. He clashed with our father who felt
fighting should be left to the poor with so little
to lose. My brother drew himself upright, defying
Father for the first time in his life. It was done—
he had volunteered to fight for the Union.
Let cowards cower behind wealth, he was going to war.

The Beginning of War

For days, my mother would not leave her room,
and the wailing drifted through the walls, down
the hall, until I thought I might go mad. Her sad
lament cast a pall over the house, as if black crepe
of death were already covering the mirrors, portals
to the other side. At last, she left her lair. Her hair
was groomed, face washed as if nothing unusual
had occurred. The first words out of her mouth
were commands to the servants. There was work
to be done. My sisters and their children, left alone
by husbands, fathers, who also felt duty bound,
converged on our house, and the air was filled
now with laughter, as if we were all on holiday
at Bar Harbor, running along the rocky shores,
chasing waves. We all believed this uprising
would be short-lived, suppressed by our men
who had God and manufacturing on their side.
And so we read aloud, played games, joined
in singing a new song, "Aura Lea," while Ann's
fingers made the keys weep, warbling in unison
about the blackbird in the willow tree. And we
had no idea how many tears, how many years,
lay before us before the men would march home.

Homefront

My sisters finally moved home when reality
of war settled over us like a fine dust. The North
was not to win within weeks, as we had all believed.
The news, as printed in the *Post* and the *Transcript,*
tried hard to rouse the spirits of Bostonians,
but battle after battle, our men were left on Southern
soil. The women would gather each afternoon
to do their part in the war effort. Cook created cakes
and breads that could be sent to the front, while
Mother, Sisters, and I decorated their wrappings.
We had never learned to can or bake, and gardens
were only meant for flowers in our circle, useless
skill when soldiers could not eat rose petals.
The Ladies' Aid Society sent out the word
that each of us should be knitting socks, gloves,
since winter would be raging soon. Our needles
clicked for hours, and when we were not knitting,
we were mending blankets, embroidering quilts.
The only relief was when the Society organized
a fair or a musical performance to raise funds
for medical supplies. But most of our days
were knotted together with needle and thread.

Confession

Father's days were long with Charles gone to war.
One night as he sat, hands cupping head at his desk,
oil lamp lighting the lines in his face, I entered,
closing the door softly. He looked surprised to see me
in his masculine domain, but I was not deterred.
I knelt by his side, took his hand in mine. Confession
spilled from my lips as I explained that Charles
and I had conspired to work together on business
decisions, deals that he had struck were not just luck
of a young man coming into his own, but were in fact
my ideas, as much as his. When Father gasped,
grabbed back his hand as if I had set fire to him,
I held up my palm, calmed him with my soothing
tone. As proof, I recited a litany of transactions
I had committed to memory. His face transformed
from horror and disbelief, to amazement. A woman
should not be able to hold figures in her head
as easily as she held a teacup in her lap. Leaning
back in his chair, he let out a loud breath. I stood,
straightened my shoulders, informed him of my plan
to report to his office in town tomorrow. My war
contribution would no longer consist of knitting
and purling but of using the brain beneath my curls.

The Agreement

My father refused to let me accompany him downtown,
but he agreed to let me use his desk at home, to give
me the accounts that had once been Charles' burden.
He brought home first a few files, but once he saw
my efficiency, my way of organizing accounts
as if I were arranging the drawers in a sideboard,
he stacked more and more on his desk, never
speaking of what I was doing, as if it were illegal
or immoral. My mother did not ask where I spent
my days, while she and my sisters sewed away
week after week. Father must have sworn her
to secrecy, a silence that surely weighed heavily
on her. For the first time in my life, confined
in my father's paneled library, I felt freedom.
For the first time in my life, I felt necessary,
not just an ornament waiting to be hung
from the arm of a husband, but a woman of worth.

The Letter

Our days hinged upon the hinge of the mail slot
Father had installed in the front door before the War.
Now we waited each day for letters to slide
onto the polished floor, letters from Charles, chatty
and lighthearted, as if he were taking a respite
in the South in order to bask in the sunshine, hiding
the horrors I suspected he saw each day. My sisters
always brought their own letters to our house
before opening them so we could share the news
together. But one day, Margaret entered, looking
pale, clutching an envelope from her husband's
commanding officer. She asked that I read it aloud,
her hand shaking too much to hold the single sheet.
The first sentence began that John was still alive.
A collective sigh filled the parlor, and I continued
to read that he had sustained a wound to his leg,
requiring its removal. Margaret did not cry or scream
but only repeated that he was alive. Being maimed
did not matter as long as he had a breath, defeated death.

The War Ends

When the fifth April of war began, our hope
was stretched as thin as a spider web—still
glistening with morning dew, but in danger
of being wiped away. The weeks spent
preparing for balls and cotillions seemed silly
now that life was somber and uncertain. Why
worry about the proper dance step or escort
when so many men had lost their legs, arms,
lives? I did not realize how long laughter had ceased
until I heard the ringing of a young girl's voice,
bright as a knife against crystal, and then pealing
of church bells, over and over. I rose from Father's
desk and rushed out the door, Mother and Sisters
trailing behind. Everyone was shouting, horses
rearing at the pandemonium. The war was over.
Merchants locked their shops, children poured
out of school doors, banks shuttered. Everywhere
were flags—hung from trees, draping doorways.
The Commons was flooded with people, faces
tear-stained and joyous at once. Cooks dashed
back to kitchens to retrieve picnic baskets, wine,
while the crowd sang "The Battle Cry of Freedom."
That evening, I sat on a blanket with my family
and watched as fireworks meteored the skies.
Just as ancients once found comets to be omens,
I took these explosions as promises, portents.

Charles Returns

The war was not over like the extinguishing
of a candle, but rather like a well-banked fire
that crackles, glows, long after the flame has ebbed.
It was many weeks before Charles made his way home.
He tried to hide the horrendous memories he had locked
away inside, but when he wrapped his arms around me
in a brotherly hug, I felt the weight of war radiate
from him. Father was thrilled to have his hero home,
and he wasted no time in replacing me with Charles.
I did not mind since my brother was to marry soon.
For the past five years, he had exchanged letters
with Laurel, a girl who lived just blocks away,
someone who seemed too young when he met her
at a ball before the war, but at twenty-one, was now
one of the lucky women who would wed. Thousands
would remain maids, like me. So sad to think
of multitudes of young men who should be marrying,
fathering, who instead fertilized the soil, only seeds
of grass and weeds springing forth from them.

Part II

The After Time

For many women, it was difficult to return to life
as it had been before the War. Just as it is hard
to cage a wild bird, so the women found themselves
beating against the bars of society's expectations
after experiencing the freedom of independence.
They had worked, sometimes outside the home,
had balanced the household duties and the accounts
without the steady hand of their husbands. Still,
they could not vote, could not hold political office.
Little wonder that women began to organize,
to fight for their rights. And the men, no longer
soldiers, also fought to retain their positions
of power, though some were defeated by scenes
they had seen, could never be truly whole again,
even if their bodies bore no scars. As for me,
still unmarried, life fell back into its old rhythm,
a pattern of days that repeated over and over,
and I no longer dared to dream that my time
on this earth would be composed of anything
more than the slow movement of clock hands—
nothing momentous—inching around the face.

The Invitation

Seasons came and went without fanfare. The galas
that had garnered so much attention before cannons
shattered the barricades built around our protected,
privileged lives now seemed frivolous, as lightweight
and insignificant as fluff from a pillow. At twenty-eight,
I was still young enough to miss the music, the measured
steps, the warmth of a man's gloved hand on my waist.
But I was surprised when the engraved invitation to a ball
found its way to the table in the hall. At first, I scoffed
at the idea of attending, but my mother, forever hopeful,
insisted that I go. I assumed my dress would be black
this time, proof of the death of my marriageability,
but she surprised me by choosing a bright scarlet silk,
perhaps in the same way a male cardinal attracts a mate
with his brilliant feathers. Charles and Laurel, eager
to capture the joy of courting that they had been denied,
agreed to escort me. I had no expectations as I donned
my slippers that evening, but just as the worm had spun
the filament in my ballgown's shimmering material,
so the Fates had already woven the fabric of my future.

The Meeting

It is a trick of life that when we rise in the morning,
we have no idea that the smallest twist of chance,
God's rolling of His cosmic dice, can change
the channel that the river of our days has been flowing.
One casual glance or the touch of a hand during a dance
can divert our destiny, send the future waterfalling
into territory that would have seemed beyond
imagination. That night, as I entered the hall aflame
with candlelight, aflame myself in flaming silk,
I could not know that fate waited for me, clad
in a lieutenant's dress uniform. As I stood along
the wall, watching the younger women whirl
with their partners, Charles touched my elbow,
leaned in close so I could hear above the music.
There was someone he wanted me to meet,
an Army friend, a brother in arms who risked
his life too many times to count. Charles ushered
me into the next room, put his arm on a woolen
shoulder that loomed above the other men.
When he turned, blue eyes beneath restless chestnut
curls, I felt my breath catch and hold as he held
my hand. I barely caught his name—David McWilliams.

The Dance

I must have appeared mute or mentally impaired,
the sad little sister doomed to spend her days
confined to the family attic, since I could not speak
for several seconds when he asked to sign my dance
card. But when we finally made our way to the floor,
when I stretched my hand to his shoulder, placed
the other inside his fist, I finally found my tongue
as a Viennese waltz began—not the rushed, breathless
European version, but the American kind, slowed
to a pace that allowed conversation. We traded stories
of family. I shared tales of Charles when a boy—countless
encounters with provoked wasps and annoyed, kicking
colts—tales that had David howling with laughter.
His family had come from Scotland before the Revolution,
making a name in shipping and furniture making.
He was studying law before the call to arms
but now that he had seen life and death, how important
were the petty grievances he would see each day
as a barrister? As the music slowed, ended, I bowed
to take my leave, but he asked to see my dance
card. In each slot he wrote his name with flourish.

The Ride Home

My mother, present at the ball to share chaperone
and hosting duties, was giddy all the way home,
chattering in magpie exclamations about the officer—
the tall, handsome one who so rudely dominated
my dance card, but was it not romantic to do so?
Charles defended his friend's manners, reminding
our mother that the War had changed so many things,
made some old-fashioned niceties seem silly
when so many men had wrestled with Death,
held him by his lapels and looked him in the eye.
Thousands had lost the match, so the genteel
world we had all known in the time before war
had now been replaced by a swirling sphere
of change. My head was also twirling,
spinning out of control as I tried to focus
on the words exchanged inside the carriage.
I had never before felt the flutter, the wing flap
like a tiny wren caught inside my breast,
and I laid my fist there, lest my heart
attempt to fly for the first time from its nest.

Calling Cards

For hours after we arrived home, I lay awake
humming the music that I could not banish
from my thoughts. Like reading a favorite
poem or story over and over, the words
the two of us had shared came back to me
in a chorus of memory. Now I realized
how naïve I had been to think I should seek
out a husband who would only satisfy my need
to speak freely, without any desire for desire.
Now I blushed in the dark, crushed a pillow
across my face to suffocate the sheer joy
of feeling. Truly it was prophetic that mother
had chosen a dress the color of glowing flame,
for I burned at the thought of his touch. Much
of the night I tossed until I finally fell into sleep
so deep I did not awake until a maid lightly padded
into my room to help me prepare for the noon
meal. When I was finally bathed and dressed,
I pressed my hair into place and started downstairs
to what I was sure would be a feast of teasing.
As I passed the hall table, I stopped short, gasped.
A stack of calling cards, like a snow-covered mountain
of fine linen paper, avalanched upon the table top,
and when I drew near, I could see each one engraved
with the name that was already etched on my heart.

The Gentleman Calls

Mother wasted no time in issuing an invitation
to tea the next week. For days she scurried
around the house, fluttering like a trapped
bird as she flew from room to room, moving
trinkets from mantel to table and back again
as if the position of a figurine determined
my future. She insisted that Father and Charles
attend the gathering, along with my brothers-
in-law and sisters, although I could count
on one hand the teas I had attended with men.
She had directed Cook to concoct a cavalcade
of treats to be paraded before our guest—
sandwiches with orange marmalade and pear
conserve, salted almonds, fancy biscuits,
scones, and peppermint bonbons. I begged
her to show restraint, but like a drowning
person thrashing the water to stay afloat,
she could not help herself. When the doorbell
rang on the assigned day, she had posed
our family in the parlor as if a photographer
had arrived to capture our images for eternity.
As the maid, dressed in a conspicuously crisp
dress and apron, introduced David's arrival,
my mother rose, the epitome of calm and cool,
as she accepted from him zephyr flowers—blooms
representing great expectation, anticipation.
She asked the maid to please find a vase, and turned
to introduce the young man. I did not know
whether the heart I heard beating was hers or mine.

The Tea

I do not remember much of the chatter exchanged
that day, my brother and David bantering about
their time together during the war, laughter loud
enough to cover the memories of cannon fire.
My father, usually stern and sober-faced, smiled
as the younger men sparred with saber-sharp wit.
Mother tried to steer the conversation to appropriate
tea-time repartee—weather, cotillions, music.
As for me, I was silent unless spoken to, muted
by my own desire to conceal the feelings humming
through me, my teacup rattling against its saucer.
David and I had spoken openly at the ball, but all
that ease disappeared for me, here in my own home,
as I sat hoping that my family would approve
of this man, the only one who had ever stirred
the embers banked inside my heart. When five
o'clock chimed on the mantel, David rose, thanked
my mother for her hospitality. It was my father,
though, who showed him to the door, their voices
muffled in the hall. When Father returned, he
looked at me, said he had given permission
for David to call.

Courting Begins

The first day we were to stroll together, I feared
my feet would not meet the ground. Julia agreed
to be my chaperone, and I knew she was still young
enough to remember the thrill of courtship, staying
close behind us, but far enough to feign deafness.
When David arrived, he was attired in soft gray
that played with the blue of his eyes. My mother
had selected my dress, a green silk with tiny
tassels trimming the bodice hem. As we walked
away from my house, I had a strange premonition
that I would never return, and perhaps I did not,
not as the same person I had been. But I shook
away the eerie feeling, trying to find the light
rapport we had felt in our first meeting. Passing
a cart filled with nosegays, David stopped, dropped
coins into the vendor's hand, more than required,
and chose yellow roses, indicating friendship,
for Julia, but mine were red, symbol of romance,
passion, love. If only time could have frozen
in that moment, the clock hands clasped forever,
my life would have been long enough.

Love Grows

Even now, after all these years, those days
when our love had just been planted, sprouting
green and bud-like, make my heart ache
with remembrance, desire, regret. Strolls
gave way to lazy picnics in the park, sharing
gingerbread and stories of childhood, which led
to concerts and dances, always with a sister
chaperoning. Catching glimpses of a couple
in a window, I gasped to realize I was half
of the dashing duo, two people so perfectly
matched in their juxtaposition—he brash
and broad-shouldered, while my head reached
just high enough to rest on his chest if such signs
of affection had been allowed. When young,
I had thought that Charles carried the sun,
but now I came to realize that his glow
was more moonlike, compared to David's
radiance, so strong that people he did not know
sometimes stared, as if he were a star
of the stage. Sometimes at night, sleep
escaping me, I would go to my knees
and thank God for this turn of fortune,
this gift, that I did not understand, deserve,
but I had no way of knowing then
how undeserving I truly was.

December

Spring bloomed into summer, which faded
into autumn's umber, and finally the early
gloaming of winter. For months there had been
family dinners, afternoons of croquet on the lawn,
hours of Whist or Bridge, Charades or Pass the Slipper
on days when weather confined us inside. Some days
we sang as Ann played, and David's voice blended,
entwined with mine as if they were warp and weft.
One day in late November, he arrived for dinner,
beaming from cold and excitement. Mr. Dickens
had arrived in Boston on a reading tour, and David
had procured four tickets—two for us, two for Charles
and Laurel. Given that the event was to take place
on the second day of December, I only had a few days
to prepare my ensemble. When the evening arrived,
we exited our carriage at the Tremont Temple, surrounded
by crowds attempting to buy tickets that did not exist.
David whispered as we walked to our seats, pointing out
with a subtle nod, Longfellow, Emerson. A large maroon
backdrop graced the stage, along with a waist-high
desk, a block on top for resting an elbow. When the author
took his place and finally quieted the Bostonian crowd,
which had forgotten its proud reserve, I could see
in the glow of gas lights that he looked like a man
who was too tired to perform. But when he began reading
A Christmas Carol, becoming each character in turn,
I lost all awareness of him. When he reached the speech
of Bob Cratchit, speaking to his small son, I used
my handkerchief to capture the tears before they spotted
my bodice. In the darkness, I could feel David watching
me, then he gently raised my gloved hand and placed
a kiss as soft as the silk itself. It was a scandalous
action, but when I looked around, there were flocks
of white handkerchiefs fluttering through the crowd
like a dule of doves. No one had noticed.

Christmas

Christmas was special that year. As we trimmed
the tree with candles, cranberries, and gingerbread
men, I was so overcome with joy that I thought
at first I must have had more than my limit
of mulled wine, but one smile from David
assured me that the headiness I felt was love
of this man and not the effects of fermented
grape. We younger members of the family
bundled up with furs and muffs and scarves.
Then we went from door to door, caroling,
accepting gifts of candies and cookies. Home
again, we opened our gifts to each other.
The monogrammed handkerchiefs and knitted
scarf I had made seemed trite when compared
to David's gifts to me—an ornate silver
jewelry box with my initials engraved on top
and a slender volume of *A Christmas Carol,*
in which Mr. Dickens had signed his name.
Just like the nephew in the book, I felt
that this Christmas was a time when I finally
opened my shut-up heart freely. How
could I know that before another year
had passed, I would instead bear such burden,
like another character, forced to wear
the chains I forged in this life?

Engagement

My beloved Vivia—
Will you please accept and wear the accompanying ring—
ruby like the gown you were wearing when I first saw you—
as a pledge of the endless love and affection of

> *Your idolizing*
>
> *David*

My Dear David—
You need no assurance from me that your valuable
gift will be doubly precious to me, as a token of your
affection. May our love, like your ring, have no end.

> *Your loving*
>
> *Vivia**

*These letters were altered from examples found in *Gaskell's Compendium of Form: Social, Educational, Legal, & Commercial,* first published by Donohue, Henneberry, & Co., 1880.

At Last

I was to find out later that David had spoken to Father
over the Christmas holiday, so by the time the New Year
clock chimed the hour of beginnings, we were engaged.
My mother kept hugging me, drawing my left hand
to her face over and over, exclaiming, *At last! At last!*
If I were to be honest, it did not seem real to me,
either. For so many years, I had been overlooked,
undervalued, and now a man—not just any man—
but a man of beauty and brains, of wealth and worth,
had chosen me to be his bride. I tended to glide
through the days in a daze until my mother scolded
that I must snap out of my stupor and begin planning.
There was so much to do in a short window of time
if we were to be married in spring. First, the dinner
with family members, the toasting and tears. David's
parents had been dead for many years, and an only
child, he had a mere scattering of aunts, uncles,
cousins with whom to share his news. I, however,
had a horde of family and friends who would ruffle
if left out. Mother and I spent hours listing
names of those receiving betrothal cards.
When the last was finally sent, I went to my room
and fell onto a cloud of feathers. But instead of sleeping
soundly, I kept dreaming that I was running, running
on a battlefield with cannon blasts and gunfire
all around me. I kept shouting that I could not die
because I had to get married, but when I reached
the church and my groom, dressed in an officer's
best, turned to me, he wore a skeleton's face.
My scream escaped the confines of my dream.

Preparations

I had no more nightmares, so tired each night
that I barely had energy to extinguish the light.
My days were a blur of shopping and decisions—
selections of fabrics and flowers, cakes and candles.
The invitations had to be printed and posted,
along with a newspaper article about our pending
nuptials. My sisters were to be my matrons
of honor, and Charles was to act as best man.
The wedding would be held at our church,
followed by a luncheon in our backyard.
Endless lists filled my days—menus, wedding
favors, thank you gifts. I rarely saw David,
and when I did, he smiled weakly, avoided
any questions about the special day. I assumed
that all men acquiesced to the bride, avoided
opinions that might cause strife. It is one of life's
lessons that I learned too late, to listen to one's
inner voice, even if it whispers words that you
do not want to hear. If only once I had taken
his hand and asked him to unburden his mind.
If only once I had asked him to speak freely.
If only—two words that must echo in hell.

The Dress

My mother declared that my dress was a decade
in the making, so I should only have the best—
a Charles Frederick Worth original. I thought
Worth an appropriate name for the Englishman
who claimed Paris as his home, for his gowns
were extravagant in style and cost. But Mother
was determined that my wedding would cause
all of the other mothers in Boston to secretly
seethe because mine was the finest of the season.
The gown was a cloud of satin and tulle, trimmed
with rows of ruffles, and bows on the sleeves.
The train trailed out the bustled back, supporting
the lace veil. I had never considered myself
a beauty, but when the dress arrived, and I tried
it on to be fitted, I was transformed. Empress
Eugenie and Queen Victoria were no better
attired than I. Looking back now, it was a fairy
tale, a little girl's dream, no more substantial
than vapor, an exhalation on a winter morn.

Final Preparations

Etiquette demanded that I not go out
for amusement once I had accepted
the marriage proposal, but I barely noticed,
my days a haze, a flurry of final preparations.
David was wraithlike, passing through the house
at Sunday dinners or to meet Charles for an evening
out. The warmth we had shared—so nearly a spark,
promise of a flame—was tamped down by society's
insistence that we distance ourselves until after
the nuptials, and I promised myself that once wed,
desire would be rekindled, fanned to a blaze.
One of the last tasks I completed before our wedding
day was to choose a gift for my groom—a golden
pocket watch etched with thistle, homage to his Scottish
roots, and inside I had engraved:
D.—My love for you is timeless. V.

Wedding Morning

The morning I was to wed, my mother entered
my room, sat on the edge of my bed, and cradled
my hand. She was there for the talk that all mothers
were required to give so their daughters understood
what was expected on their wedding nights. I cast
my eyes down, pretended to be shocked, portrayed
the role that Miss Janice had warned me to play
years before when she taught me anatomy, showed
me drawings and illustrated in academic terms
what most women only whispered about. Mother
spoke of fulfilling female duties, bearing unbearable
humiliation for the sake of marital harmony. Women
must allow men unthinkable acts if they wanted
to keep them from straying. And, of course, wives
became mothers as a reward for their submission.
How different Miss Janice's version had been—
ardor, desire, fulfillment. I vowed then to live out
my own vows, to always follow the path of passion.

At the Church

My conveyance to the church was an open carriage,
festooned with swags of roses and lilies. Ann rode
with me, helping to control the veil and layers
of fabric, intent on floating away upon the May Day
breeze. The rest of my family had traveled ahead,
hoping to have everyone seated before I arrived,
making an entrance grand enough for a coronation.
My mother had invited half the city, the half
composed of those with wealth and status. Never
did she ask my opinion about the epic nature
of the wedding. This was to be her last to plan,
and it was to be grand. As we approached, Father
left the steps of the church and helped me down
as gracefully as possible with a train that trailed
several feet behind when dropped. His face looked
lined in the sunlight, and I asked him if everything
was all right. He assured me that all would be fine.
He took my hand, and Ann followed behind, arms
full of satin and tulle. We mounted the steps, stopping
at the top, waiting for Wagner to begin, signaling
my march. Suddenly, a little boy, taking two steps
at a time, started calling, *Miss! Miss!* as he waved
a paper toward me. Ann shouted for him to stop,
to be careful not to touch, but I took the note,
opened it, and read. Then the words dissolved,
the ink ran liquid once more, filling my head.

The Note

My Dearest Vivia—

Know first of all that my love for you is true,
and it is for that reason that I have made this decision
today. When I first met you, I was swept away by your
charms, and those feelings of deep affection and respect
have not waned. It is I. I am the person who has transformed over
the past year.

Returning from the War, I thought I could be content to succeed in
business as our own accomplished fathers, but in recent months, I
have been burdened with a desire to return to the military.

Many of my fellow soldiers are serving in the West—a wild,
untamed region to which I could not possibly ask you to
accompany me. It is a place filled with adventure but also
unthinkable dangers. However, if I did not follow my heart and re-
join my comrades, I fear that I would be asking you to spend your
life married to a man consumed with regret and unhappiness.

So, dear Vivia, I must ask, no, beg you to forgive me for leaving
you today, a day that should have been joyful. You might ask why I
did not tell you sooner. It is because I am a dreadful coward—not
on the battlefield but in your sweet presence. Please do not hate me
but remember the love we have shared.

Still Yours—

David

Limbo

For days I lay in a state of limbo—somewhere
between life and death, wakefulness and sleep.
I caught fragments of phrases like bitter snowflakes
drifting down upon me—Charles threatening to beat
someone, my mother sobbing that the shame would kill
me . . . or her. Random hands spooned warm broth
between my dry lips, but I did not open my eyes, eyes
that could not face the expressions of pity. Had I still
possessed the arsenic wafers my mother had purchased
for my complexion, I would have dragged myself
from the bed long enough to devour the entire box,
before climbing back beneath the quilt, pulling it over
me like sod, and giving way to the eternal sleep I craved.
One afternoon, I thought I was dreaming when I opened
my lids long enough to capture a vision of Miss Janice,
clad in a smart emerald green day dress, sitting straight
in a needlepoint chair next to me. I must have gasped
because she moved to my bed, took my hand in hers—
solid and real. Leaning close to my ear she whispered,
*It was your own Mr. Dickens who wrote, "We need
never be ashamed of our tears."* And so at last
I let loose a sob from so deep within myself,
that it felt as if a poisonous root had been ripped
out of my chest, allowing the healing to begin.

Coming Back

Each day, Miss Janice—now Mrs. Owen—came
to my room. Father had sent for her as a last
grasp at my recovery. Her step-sons were away
at school, and as a rule, her husband spent
hours at the mills, so her days were usually
filled with Whist and a wish for purpose.
Years of separation had not parted our spirits,
and it was her strength, her determination,
that brought me to my feet again, as if she
had poured her own fierce blood into my body.
She let me know that my sisters had rallied
round, writing notes and returning gifts. Mother
was beginning to emerge from her room
and had even attended two or three teas,
where she garnered so much sympathy
that it overshadowed the humiliation, shame.
On days when it felt as if my heart
was bruised beyond repair, Miss Janice—
for that is who she would always be to me—
would let me cry, my head cradled on her
shoulder. One dark day, she shared her story,
one I had never heard. At eighteen, she had fallen
in love, had fallen out of virtue with a young
man she was betrothed to, but two weeks
before they were to wed, he ran away
with an expectant servant girl he had also
taken to bed. His parents were horrified
and disowned their son, but Miss Janice,
broken at first, gathered all the pieces
of her soul, glued them back together,
and wore her scars proudly like ancient
Japanese pottery that, although broken,
derives its worth and beauty from being
reconstructed with gilding.

Still

A fortnight had passed when I finally rose up
from my bed, bathed in a tub that the maid
filled with water so warm I could barely sit,
and washed my long hair, using a comb
to untangle the knots. I refused to let grief—
for I did grieve everything I had lost as if
David had been slain in battle—kill
me. I would not become a recluse, a little
gray spider lurking in the corner of my room.
But just as I was feeling stronger than I had
in two weeks, I noticed a folded paper placed
carefully under the handle of my hand mirror.
I did not know who had rescued the letter
as I lay unconscious, but now it was here,
haunting, taunting me again. My first desire
was to build a fire, turning his words to ashes,
just like my own did inside my mouth when I
spoke of him. But I knew I could not destroy
this last vestige of our love. My hands shook
as I opened, smoothed the paper and read.
This time, there was no shock, and so I carefully
mouthed each word. Phrases played across
the page: *My Dearest Vivia, my love for you
is true, Still Yours.* And as I read, his reason
for going west without me echoed as honestly
being a desire to keep me sheltered, safe. But
I was not a delicate orchid praying for protection.
Perhaps I had played the role of dainty debutante
too thoroughly, leading him to believe that I was
made of silk instead of steel. In that moment,
I knew what I must do.

Military Office

Miss Janice had told me that she had an engagement
the next day, and so she would visit after noon.
Father was at his office in town, and Mother
had joined my sisters for a morning of shopping,
followed by a luncheon. I took the opportunity
to slip into my clothes and slip out the back
door unseen. Wearing a hat with a wide brim,
I kept my face shadowed from those who might
recognize me, call out their condolences. Numerous
times since the beginning of the War, I had walked
past the Army office, paying no attention. Today,
I was determined to find answers. When I entered,
an older man in uniform, a veteran, no doubt,
sat at a desk with a stack of papers before him.
There was no bustle since we were now at peace.
Politely, I told him that I was looking for my intended,
a lieutenant who had gone west. He listened, shook
his graying head, and told me he could not help.
He was not authorized to give me information,
even though I flashed my ruby ring in his face
as proof of my story. I noticed a younger soldier
at a nearby table, but he lowered his head. Tears
spilled from frustration, but the older man was stone.
I dragged my feet back home, but this was the end
of the battle, not the war. I would return.

Success

Miss Janice and I began to take strolls in town,
bringing back tender memories of childhood.
I always made excuses to walk past the Army
office, but day after day, the same man drowsed
behind his desk. At last, we walked by and I
could see that the young man, the one who hung
his head on that first day, had taken the place
of the marble-faced man. Miss Janice had ducked
inside a shop to pick out a gift for her husband's
birthday, so I slipped inside the office and caught
the young man off guard. Throwing etiquette
out the window, I grasped his hand, and pled
with him to tell me where David had been sent.
The poor boy was so aghast that he gasped
out that he knew my fiancé, one of a group
that had been sent to Ft. Gibson in Indian Territory,
a God-forsaken place in the wilderness filled
with savages and mosquitoes, no place for a lady.
But he did not know this female, fervent
as Saint Joan and just as determined to complete
my mission, martyred or not.

Mapping My Way

Now my path forward was clear,
my future carved out for me like a rock canyon
cut by water, but I had never ventured farther
than Miss Porter's. I knew nothing about the West
or what lay between it and Boston. My first task
was to procure a map. My father's library, stacked
with books that he rarely had time to peruse, beckoned.
Filed between the histories and biographies of great
men stood an atlas. Thankfully, it was a newer
version, a gift from a son-in-law last Christmas
At first, I thought of removing only the pages
which might prove important, but I could not bring
myself to tear the maps from their bindings.
Quietly, I made my way up the stairs to my room.
When I opened the book to a full picture
of the United States, I knew it was a deceptive
depiction of the true distance that lay between
David and me, perhaps an omen of the separation,
the chasm that loomed between us. But chasms
could be crossed if strong bridges were built.

A Plan Emerges

In those days before I left, I floated
like fluff blown from a dandelion,
buoyed by the idea that David truly loved me.
I would find him, present the groom's gift
that still ticked away like an abandoned heart,
marking the time until it could lie in the jacket's
chest pocket of its rightful owner. He would be
amazed that I had traversed over twelve hundred
miles, would draw me to him in the type of embrace
I had always longed for but refrained from, due
to convention's constraints. Away from civilization,
we could marry simply, live simply, love simply.
But first, I had planning to do. I hinted to my mother
that Claire, my friend from Miss Porter's, had asked
that I plan an extended visit at her home in Hartford.
Married, she had birthed her third child, a little girl
she named after me. The trip might take my mind
off the ordeal I had suffered. Mother, if truth be told,
was thrilled at removing me from Boston. I was
a constant reminder of the humiliation, made worse
by Mother's own hubris prior to the wedding day.
People love the myth of Icarus because they like
to see the mighty fall.

Taking Leave

Money was no issue. Although I had never held
a position outside the home, Charles slipped bills
into my hand each month, small stipends for work
I did behind the back of our father. I needed
nothing for myself, so apart from gifts I purchased
for others, the money was untouched, tucked away
in a wooden box under a board in the floor beneath
my bed. Now it felt like a treasure chest, a pirate's
bounty, and I was the brigand who was escaping
with it. I wrote a letter to Claire, announcing the day
I would arrive, and one to Miss Janice, thanking
her for the kindness she had shown the past weeks,
but I would be leaving the city for an undetermined
time. I did not pack my trove of gowns, knowing
that I would need sturdier stuff than silk, satin.
I was hoping Mother did not inspect my armoire
and question why I had left behind my best.
My father arranged for Samuel to transport me
and my luggage to Claire's home. As I said goodbye
to my family, I studied each face as I never
had before. I have come to believe that we
rarely look at a loved face thoroughly—until
we realize we might never gaze upon it again.

The Arrival

The journey to Hartford was uneventful, and I let
myself believe that my sojourn to the West could be
as smooth. Claire took me in her arms, excited to share
her home and family. Her two oldest clambered
about the house like spring lambs, while Little Vivia
quietly fed at her mother's breast or listened intently
as her young nurse lullabied her to sleep, snagging
my heart with a memory of Aideen. Alone, Claire
cradled my hands and told me again how sorry
she was about the wedding. I could no longer keep
my secret from her, and my plan tumbled out.
Her face grew pale, and she began to beg me
to reconsider. How could a woman travel alone?
How could I survive storms and dangers of every
stripe? How could I find my way without a guide?
I waited for her to pause. Nothing, I assured her,
could be as horrible as the heartbreak I had borne.
Now I had the chance to mend it, to convince
David that I would rather live in a tent with him
than to sleep alone in my father's mansion. *Please,*
I begged, *help me find the happiness you hold.*
Claire wrapped me in a firm hug and wept softly.
She would help me prepare, but alarm bells
were sounding inside her, warning that my mission
was a terrible mistake. My love overruled all reason.

Gathering Begins

It felt as if we were re-living our school days
as Claire and I walked arm in arm down streets,
into shops and cafes. Every day she kindly
requested that I reconsider, but she knew
that nothing, not even the affection I felt for her,
deeper than that for my blood sisters, could alter
my path. With money, seemingly impossible endeavors
became trivial. Claire's stable boy was tasked
with procuring a hearty horse and swift carriage,
the type physicians drove to emergencies, appropriate
in describing my own plight. He brought back
a strong sorrel, named Pleasant—Pleas for short—
due to his likeable disposition, and a carriage
that had belonged to a local doctor who died
when he ignored his own grippe. When Claire
asked how I proposed to travel alone, I showed
her the hat my mother had worn to my grandmother's
funeral, large and black with heavy veil. Even ruffians
might hesitate to accost a mourning widow. Claire
was not convinced. She unlocked a box she kept
at the back of her sideboard. Matthew, her oldest
brother, had never returned from the War, lost
in one of the last battles—Appomattox. His gun
came home without him. Now she tenderly
held out the pistol. When I protested, she insisted.
Perhaps it would bring good luck, and her boys
would never be forced to fight for freedom.

Gathering Continues

My nights were filled with writing letters and lists.
I felt that I should explain myself to each family
member and Miss Janice. My words seemed hollow
even to me, like a chrysalis after the butterfly's
escape. Charles would attempt to find me, of this
I was sure, and so Claire had promised not to post
the missives until I had had time to reach a place
outside their reach. The lists were of items
I would need on my journey, keeping in mind all
must fit into a small leather trunk attached to the back
of the carriage and a large carpet bag for clothing.
During the day, Nate, Claire's stable boy, instructed
me on how to harness the horse, a task I found easy.
Harder was the handling of the Colt. Claire and I
would take rides to the country, with Nate manning
the reins. Once away from houses, he set up targets—
bottles on stumps—and showed me how to load
the paper cartridges, to cock the hammer, squeeze
the trigger. At first, I was nearly knocked off
my feet, but with time, I learned to brace myself,
to steady both hands on the wooden grip, to breathe
only when I heard the bottles break. Never
could I imagine the shattering that was yet to come.

Part III

The Journey Begins

Finally, my preparations were complete. How easy
it would have been to stay with Claire. But every
day that passed only increased my need to reach
David, to convince him that I was strong enough
to live amid the barren prairie as long as I was
living with him. The day I left, Claire followed
me to the carriage, but when *Please* escaped
her mouth, I put my gloved finger to her lips,
and she wrapped me in her arms instead.
As I drove away, I could feel her waiting
for me to disappear amid conveyances
crowding the street or to become a black dot,
growing smaller and smaller as I headed west,
the same direction the sun took each evening,
a sun that never looked back. I was dressed
in black and wore the veil over my pale face
as I let Pleas set his own pace. I did not know
how many miles we might cover in one day,
since, like the path I had chosen in life,
so much depended on circumstance, chance.

The Plan

My widow's weeds were growing warm in the early
summer sun. As soon as I was away from town, I drew
back the veil, but every time a wagon or carriage met
me on the road, I masqueraded myself again. Men
lifted their hats, mumbled condolences, and I felt
a dram of guilt for my deceit. My plan was to make
my way to New York, then journey on to Pennsylvania,
catching an Ohio River steamboat at port in Pittsburgh.
I remembered reading accounts of the *Miami*,
whose boiler exploded, leaving two hundred dead,
and the *G.A. Thompson* that struck a snag and burned
only months before, taking seventeen souls. But river
travel seemed safer for a woman alone. Horrors greater
than fire and water awaited those foolish enough to flout
society's statutes, and I was one of the imprudent,
risking my very skin to traverse half the country.
Nothing could convince me, however, to turn back,
to turn my back on the only chance I would ever
have at recovering my only love.

The Trip to New York

I enjoyed the sound of Pleas' hooves—*clip, clop,*
clip, clop—rhythmic like a metronome, so hypnotic
I found the sound lulled me into a near-sleep,
a trance. The hours linked arms like invisible
spirits and faded into days. I stopped at reputable-
looking inns, ones with a nice stable where Pleas
could rest and be rejuvenated for the next day.
With a ring on my finger and mourning dress,
no one questioned my solitary trip. Just as echoes
of my horse's feet lulled me to nap, so the first two
days lulled me into the trap of believing that every
day would pass without worry or care. But the third
day found the sun suddenly blotted by a billowing
mass, roiling like waves bringing ashore the prow
of a thunderhead from the west. The only shelter
I could find was a copse of oak trees. Rumblings
sent an alarm through Pleas, and I knew I must
tether him quickly, lest he bolt at lightning. Before
we could reach refuge, the rain sent its spears,
and hail pelted us with pellets that felt like tiny
shots from a cannon. Once inside our sanctuary,
I tied Pleas securely, crooned to him that all
would be well. But my dress was heavy, dripping
with water. I pulled around me the blanket
I had brought for Pleas, the damp wool smelling
of hay and horse hair. The storm was unrelenting,
and I could understand why ancient people attributed
this type of fury to gods. Wind blew the rain sideways,
and I covered my head, crouched at the base of a tree
as flashes filled the air around us. I do not know
how long we cowered beneath the canopy of branches,
but when the storm finally passed, the afternoon

was moving into evening. I had to find us a place
to stay. For some reason, I could not stop shivering,
even though the storm left no coolness. Putting hand
to head, I realized that I was on fire. No wonder
I had felt as if I journeyed in a dream. I had been sick
before, and now I was drenched, nearly delirious.
To the rhythm of Pleas' steps, softened by slosh,
I kept mumbling, *A fool's errand. A fool's errand.*

Rescued

I woke lying in a feather bed, so soft it was a struggle
to sit. Instead of the black I had brought from Boston,
I was wearing a white cotton gown with ruffled cuffs.
A round-faced woman entered the room with a tea
tray and greeted me as if I were a long-lost cousin.
When I suddenly put my hand to my chest, searching
for the pouch I had sewn into my bodice, the sac
secreting my stash of money, she patted my arm,
assured me that all was well. It was then I saw, hanging
from a peg in the room, my dress, cleaned and pressed.
She said her name was Violet, and she had been caring
for me for nearly three days, ever since my horse
had brought me, lying across the carriage seat,
to her husband Henry as he worked in the garden.
The fever had fueled some thrashing dreams, dreams
in which I called out for and talked to my late husband,
but the fever's hold had broken, and I had slept
silently the night before. At first, I started to tell
her that I had never been married, but I quickly
remembered my ruse, the ring and widow's wear.
I thanked her and asked how far I was from New York.
She told me I was only a couple hours or so away
from the city. In fact, she and Henry made the trip
four times a month in the summer, delivering produce
to Delmonico's. I could hear the pride in her voice,
for the restaurant was one of the best in the world,
and their plates would be laden with her potatoes.
They were leaving again in the morning, and if I felt
well enough, I was welcome to ride in the wagon
with my carriage and horse hitched behind. When
she asked my name, I, wanting to hide my identity,
thought for only a second before saying *Gracie,*
a name formed from the Latin for *thankful.*

New York

The wagon was weighed down with baskets
and burlap bags. I crawled into the back,
smiling to myself that this kind couple
had no idea that just a few weeks prior
I had made a grand entrance in an open
carriage covered in flowers, clad in a gown
that cost more than their toil would bring
to them in a year. Now, here I was, wedged
between cartons of carrots and bags of beans.
The day was surprisingly cool, and the ride
was enjoyable. When we finally approached
the city with its towering buildings and bustle
of crowds, my old determination returned.
I leaned forward and asked Henry to please
take me to The Fifth Avenue Hotel. Drawing
the horses to a halt, he asked if I was sure,
not convinced that the fever had deserted
my brain. I assured him that my family
had stayed there on more than one occasion.
When we arrived at the building, brick clad
with white marble trim, Henry helped me down
and told me that he would make arrangements
for Pleasant and my carriage at a nearby stable.
As I gathered my bag, I stopped where Violet
sat, still unconvinced. *Thank you for saving me.*
I took her hand in mine, placed in her palm
several folded bills. When she started to protest,
I turned toward the doors where my old life lived.

The Fifth Avenue Hotel

A woman alone in New York did not draw attention
as it did in Boston, so I felt no need to plead my case
for needing a room. I would lie if I said that I did not
feel at home in the hotel with its rich carpet, its heavy
masses of gilt, its rosewood and brocatelle settees.
No wonder the Prince of Wales had said the hotel
was larger and more handsome than Buckingham Palace.
A lift took me to the fifth floor where I had my own
private bath and a view of the city, a city in a state
of constant construction. The first day, I luxuriated
in the lavishness, the opulence, that I had once failed
to notice because it was so familiar. The next morning,
I made my way to a dress shop where ready-made
garments graced the windows. I had never worn
a dress not made for me alone, but I strode inside
and chose a second mourning dress. Now I could change
if the rain caught me unaware. On the third day,
I spent time in reflection, searching my heart for direction.
This was the point after which I could not return.
My journey so far had proven that my excursion
was going to be an arduous one, but it was ardor
that had started me down this path, ardor that prodded
me forward.

A Plan Revisited

I overheard two gentlemen talking in the lobby
of the hotel, exclaiming about the train service
between Philadelphia and Pittsburgh. In fifteen
hours, they could travel over terrain that had taken
weeks on foot, no worries about raging rivers
or climbing heights. One, dapper in his stovepipe
hat, was going to return to Pittsburgh in a fortnight,
catching a steamboat that would deliver him west,
to Louisville, where a business venture awaited.
Although I had pored over my father's maps,
I had not carefully calculated how I might scale
mountains or navigate rivers. In my haste to run
away from my shame, to run toward my chance
at love, I had not stopped to anticipate the great
natural obstacles, God's impediments, placed
in my way, as if He were warning me to go
home. But I would not have listened to anyone,
not even if, like ancient prophets, I had heard
God's voice beckoning to me in wind or flame.

The Road to Philadelphia

I felt light as I climbed onto the carriage seat,
seeing New York for the last time. My plan
was set. Pleasant would be my companion
only as far as Philadelphia, where I would board
a train to Pittsburgh. Summer was still young.
Honeysuckle, sending out bee-sweet scents,
and trumpet vine, blaring orange, dripped
from trees and fences. Even the tulip trees
still clung to blossoms, green with orange
tongues. The road was lined with columbine,
heavy-headed phlox, and ox-eye sunflowers.
We took rest under cedars, red buckeyes,
black locusts. Miss Janice had taught me
to name the flowers and trees, as if they
were friends I might someday meet. And now,
they formed a processional as I made my way,
or perhaps it was a gantlet, a gorgeous path toward
trial and misery that I passed through, unknowing.

Philadelphia

If New York hummed like an excitable young woman,
Philadelphia was her much more stoic uncle, though
the former was older by decades. Still, the atmosphere
was more subdued, serious, weighted by history
that hung in the air. I wasted no time making my way
to the depot, where I deposited eight dollars for a first-
class ticket. Since I would be leaving early the next
day, I spent my time tying up the last of my loose ends—
finding a room, arranging for my leather trunk to be sent
to the railroad station, driving Pleasant to a stable.
The owner was a kind man who stroked the horse's
nose and spoke soft words I could not hear,
but the crooning caused Pleas' ears to twitch in rhythm.
When I offered to sell the sorrel and rig, the man
hesitated, but I stated a price half of what I had paid,
and he smiled widely, offered to take me to my hotel.
I wrapped my arms around the horse's neck, let my tears
fade into his mane. He had brought me far, but now
I would ride an iron horse.

Train

I arrived at the station the next day, eager
to leave the East behind. Once we crossed
the Allegheny Mountains, I knew I would
be committed to my cause. When the porter
led me to my car, I gasped with delight to see
the velvet draperies, gilt frame mirrors, upholstered
chairs. He arranged to have fresh berries brought
to me, along with a slender flute of Champagne.
As I slipped the glass beneath my veil and sipped,
I glanced out a window. There, standing on the walk,
glancing at his pocket watch, was a man whose hair
held the sun. It took a moment or two to realize
that I was looking once more at Charles, my brother
left behind so many weeks ago. I gazed at the dear
face I thought I had seen for the last time. Was he
here on business? Had he received my letter, launched
a search? My heart lurched with a desire to descend
the train steps, throw my arms around his neck,
and plead with him to take me home. Just then,
Laurel appeared, apparently arriving on another train,
and he took her bag, shook her hand as was proper,
before leading her away. I strained to watch them
as long as I could, then sat back, my heart an anchor.

The Ride

To this day, I cannot imagine the way those less
fortunate traveled over the terrain that the train
traversed. I had, indeed, been naïve to believe
that I, even with Pleasant's heartiness, could have
scaled the slopes, forded the rivers, required
to reach Pittsburgh. At times, my breath held,
suspended, as I looked out over the vistas.
I had never experienced beauty—not in paintings,
not in poetry—to rival this natural landscape.
When the sun finally sank amid a swirl of gold
and indigo, I closed my eyes and slept, dreaming
of a place I had never been, a place where
the colors of the sunset took root and grew
into plants covering a prairie. But when I tried
to pluck one of the flowers, the brushy bloom
brought blood. I started awake, only to find
that my ride was chugging to an end. Only then
did I realize my mistake. I had not calculated
the time it would take—fifteen hours. Around
me as I emerged—night, locomotive black.
It was one hour before the midnight chime.

Pittsburgh

This was a metropolis different from any I had visited.
This was a city of rivers—Allegheny and Monongahela
intermingling, meeting the Ohio. This was a city
of smokestacks, a place forged of iron and armaments.
This was a city of steamboat crews and railroad workers,
of men who arrived to work in industry, some who lacked
industriousness. I had never been afraid of being alone
on my journey until now. Crowds dispersed quickly,
people carted away by family and friends up past bedtime.
There was a sign on the depot wall calling to travelers
to rest their weary heads at a rooming house just blocks
away, so I decided I must leave my trunk at the station,
find a refuge for the evening, and if I returned to discover
it gone, the loss was one with which I could live. Once
away from the business section with its street lights fueled
by coal gas, the darkness was too deep for shadows. Every
skittering on stone sent goose flesh up my arms. From
behind, an arm was suddenly around my neck.
Instinctively, I swung my bag, contacting the attacker,
but my reprieve was short. He came at me again,
trying to wrench the bag from my grasp, and I wished
I had the Colt, wrapped inside. As he snapped the chain
on my necklace, the one Miss Janice had given me so many
years before, I sent up a scream that echoed against walls.
To stop me, his large hand was around my throat, and I
was suddenly an animal—kicking, biting, scratching.
Just when I thought I would die on that street, I heard
shouting, then the sound of something solid striking flesh
and bone. My attacker went down with a moan, and behind
him, holding a cudgel, was a young man, no more than
fourteen or fifteen. Without asking, he grabbed my hand,
and we ran.

Toby

The boy's house was not far, and his mother waited,
freshly baked bread and cheese on the table. Knowing
he would be coming home from working on a steamboat
that had made landing that evening, she dozed
in her chair, eager to hear of his adventures. Of course,
I did not know all of this that evening as she woke,
startled to see her son enter the room with a woman.
I realize now what a sight I must have been—mourning
dress ripped at the neck, hair tangled and tousled,
blood on my face and arms. She let out an oath
then led me to a settee just as the shock settled over me.
The shaking, quaking like elm leaves, started in my knees
and reverberated upward until I could not hold the glass
of brandy she had instructed Toby, her son, to pour.
She pressed the snifter to my lips, gently tipping
so as not to spill. I could not speak, could not tell
the horror, but the boy told of the attack. Gently,
she led me to a bed, bathed my face and arms,
removed my shoes, and helped me beneath the quilts.
It was days before I could form words, syllables
sticking in my throat like the burs I had plucked
from Pleasant's mane. I was able to write *trunk*
on a piece of paper, and Toby was surprised
to find it just where I had left it a lifetime ago.

Sally

Sally had been a widow for nearly half her life,
her husband having been killed in a steamboat
explosion when Toby was first born. As strong
as the iron produced in Pittsburgh, she never
remarried, making her way as laundress, seamstress,
any job to fill the table until Toby himself was old
enough to work. When he became a cabin boy,
she cried, fearing he, too, would be lost, but Toby
loved the Ohio, and she made her peace with the river.
I stayed with Sally until I reclaimed myself, until
the bruises on my throat and inside my soul faded.
She paled when my plan to venture into an unfamiliar
land, Indian Territory, was laid out before her. Had I
not learned the lesson that a woman should not travel
alone? When I convinced her that nothing could keep
me apart from the man who had captured my heart,
she rose and returned with the scissors she used
in sewing. If I meant to make it to the wilderness,
I must lose the last of my old life, lose my very self.

Transformation

I cried as Sally cut the locks that fell in a fountain
around my shoulders and down my back. Never
before had my hair been shorn, only trimmed
with tiny snips. Now, years of pampering,
years of vanity, lay on the floor in broom-like
swirls. She handed me a mirror, and I gazed
into the face of someone I did not know. Next,
she gave me a set of Toby's clothes, faded
and worn from washing, and told me to dress,
binding my breasts with strips of linen. Boots
that had long ago been declared too small
for the boy were a perfect fit for my feet.
And I donned a soft felt hat that hid my brow.
When I walked from the bedroom, Sally
put her hands to her face in disbelief. Vivia
had died behind the door and Thomas was born.

Cabin Boy

Toby had made arrangements for me, his cousin,
to accompany him on the journey from Pittsburgh
to the Mississippi. Like him, I was to act as cabin
boy. He had even created a story, like a Dickens
novel, in which I was a poor orphan, my family
having been killed when Confederate soldiers
set our house ablaze. The scars I bore on my body
made me hide from prying eyes, so I preferred
to take my toiletries in peace. The night before
we left, I looked inside my trunk one last time,
holding the remnants of the life I had left.
I opened the pouch that I had worn against
my chest and counted the currency. Never,
as Thomas, would I need this much money.
I divided it equally, sticking half into my pocket
and the rest inside *A Christmas Carol.* Crying,
I took off the ruby ring. I found Sally sewing
in the parlor, took her hand, and placed
the ring on her finger. If I did not return in a year,
she was to keep the ring as a remembrance.
Also, I wanted her to have my second prized
possession, the signed book that brought back
such a clutching in my chest that I could barely
tell her not to open it until Toby and I embarked.
As I started to leave, she stopped me just outside
the door, reached down into her flower bed,
and with a fist full of moist earth, rubbed the dirt
into my fingernails, held my face with filthy hands.

The First Steamboat

A cabin boy's work was never-ending—helping
cook in the galley, carrying meals to the seamen
in the mess hall or to the officers in their private
quarters. Like carrier pigeons flying from one level
to another, we bounded up and down carpeted stairs,
delivering boundless messages. We learned
to stow the sails, to watch at the helm, to steer clear
of snags from fallen trees, to keep watch for sand bars.
As I moved about the vessel, with its ornate ceilings,
polished floors, rosewood Rococo furniture, leaded
glass lamps, I felt a loathing of myself, of the one
I had been. Never had I given a thought to the toil
involved in making my world revolve. The faces
of all the maids and cooks my family had employed,
had looked through all those years, lined up,
accusing each night as I tried to find sleep, in spite
of aching muscles that throbbed with memory
of each load lifted, each hour spent on my feet.
Although I sought forgiveness for my selfishness,
it eluded me, perhaps because I could never forgive
myself.

The Second Steamboat

Our journey on the Ohio was measured in weeks,
not days. At last, we docked in Cairo, Illinois,
so different from its namesake in pronunciation
and culture. Some of the cabin boys joined me
in moving from one ship to the next, from one
river to the next. But it was here I had to part
from Toby. He would be journeying home
to Pittsburgh, to his mother, while I navigated
the Mississippi, navigated the next voyage
toward my dream. I disembarked with nothing
more than a cloth bag containing a set of clothes
in which I had secured the Colt and half the money
I had brought, half I had earned. The rest I pressed
beneath Toby's pillow. What a small payment
to the boy who had saved my life, and when I watched
him, waving from the deck, I betrayed my disguise
by weeping like the woman I was. Then I wiped
my eyes with my sleeve, became Thomas once again,
and followed the other boys aboard the next boat.

The Mississippi

Mississippi comes from an Algonquin word meaning
Father of Waters, an apt name for a body of water
so powerful and broad-shouldered. In my time,
the Mississippi was awash with steamboats—
circus boats and opera boats, boats filled to brim
with gamblers, sages, and charlatans. Young boys
from passing river towns would canoe out, clown
for the passengers standing along the railing in hopes
they would drop a few coins, silver glinting like fish
scales on the bark's bottom. Although we did not worry
about pirates any longer, there were still the dangers
of the river—twists and turns, swift currents in flooding
waters, and the constant fear of fire and explosion.
But in truth, I learned to love the river, the constant
lapping of waves, the way sunlight caught in crests,
the reflection of moon and stars held in a mighty
mirror, dark and deep.

Napoleon, Arkansas

I learned that the steamboat would dock at a spot
named Napoleon, and I found it odd that a group
of settlers would choose to give their town the name
of someone who, although powerful, had ultimately
failed. But when I saw the town itself, the naming
had, indeed, been prophetic. What the Civil War
had not destroyed, the river had, its hungry waters
gnawing away at the shore like a fairy tale ogre. Half
of the boys would travel on to New Orleans, looking
for new adventures, fortune, in a city that would seem
foreign to them, but the rest of the cabin boys would join
me on the journey up the Arkansas. When I heard
their plans to venture to Ft. Gibson, to enlist in the Army,
it all became clear that I, too, should volunteer. Fear
of discovery had long ago faded. In uniform, I, at last,
could look upon David again, plan my next move,
like an emperor playing chess, mapping strategy.

The Last Boat

The soon-to-be soldiers had discussed conquering
the Arkansas in a keelboat, but the waters, worrying
at times due to stumps and snags, remained high,
prompting us to stay on as cabin boys, to steam
our way into Ft. Gibson. The summer season softened
into autumn, mellowing each day like an apple,
ripening. The passengers on this voyage varied
from the ones we had met before—young officers
from West Point, older officers trained at other posts,
civilians, merchants, and platoons of pretty women
who hoped to marry officers. Tears clutched my throat
as I watched this last group sweeping the decks, decked
out in their gowns with crinoline petticoats. But worst
was the way they touched their hair, bringing attention
to the sunlit color or to a curl. After all these months,
I had made myself believe that I did not miss being
a woman, but now I was filled with longing—longing
for my long hair, for my soft skin, for my very self.

Ft. Gibson

I had envisioned a miserable outpost, inhabited
by only the roughest of individuals. Instead,
our steamboat was greeted by a cheering crowd
of children and adults of all ages. The ground
was elevated above the river, and twin houses
with shaded porches welcomed home officers
and their wives. There were stables on a hill,
a schoolhouse, the government store, the chapel—
all whitewashed and gleaming pearlescent in the sun.
Inside an enclosure, a burial ground sat, adorned
with trees and blooming shrubs. Had it not been
for the blockhouses, the palisades with their heavy
wooden gates, one would never have guessed at first
glance that this was a fort. For the first time, a tinge
of doubt crept, thief-like, into my mind. Why would
David have thought that these conditions would be too
primitive for me? The answer was simple. He had never
seen Fort Gibson but had relied on earlier reports.
But why, when he saw the number of women sharing
their husband's lives, did he not send for me? Questions
would have to wait, for I was being swept along
with the other recruits, and very soon I would become
Private Thomas.

Reunion Deferred

For days before our arrival, I had planned my reunion
with David. As if in a stage production of *Twelfth Night,*
I recited my lines over and over, practicing the moment
when I would reveal that I was not Private Thomas
but Vivia, the woman who had loved him enough
to desert her family and friends—to travel by road
and rail and river, to suffer through storm, illness,
attack—just to see him once again. But stepping
onto the soil of Ft. Gibson, I found that my words
were caught on the wind and sailed away downriver,
from where they had come. No, I would take time
to watch him, while I wound up my courage, like
an antique clock, until the right time chimed.

Military Life

Reveille blasted from a bugle just as the Sun wiped
sleep from his eyes, rousing the garrison. After the flag
was run up to the top of the staff, we ate breakfast
before beginning our training, drills repeated again
and again, commanders barking out orders, railing
against any recruit slow in movement or speech.
I found the regimental training tedious to the point
of tears, and I was convinced that the entire purpose
of the repetition was to cause the soldiers' minds
to shut down, to go through the actions automatically
if ever in battle, taking away the ability to think
about retreat. After drills that first day, I was assigned
to work in the garden, tending vegetables and picking
produce for our dinner. Although I had never stuck
my hands into soil, pulling up green-haired carrots
or digging up a clutch of potatoes, I found solace
in the earthy aroma, the warmth of sun-soaked loam.
I was toting a basket to the kitchen when I looked
across the yard where three men stood, gesturing
as they talked. I did not need to see his face to know.
My basket slipped from my fingers, spilling the harvest,
just as my feelings poured out, tumultuous, uncontained.

Party at the Post

During times when the soldiers were free
from duties, they fished in the river, catching
catfish as large as a child, or hunted prairie chickens—
pecking, speckling the countryside by the thousands.
There was a billiards room and a theater where soldiers
performed plays they had penned themselves. As for me,
I kept to my own company most of the time, like
the stable cat, a black whisp of movement that never
allowed a touch. Word had spread from the riverboat,
rumors swirling about my family's demise at Rebel
hands, the scars I bore, so the soldiers respected
my solitary existence, and I avoided the normal
banter, the boyish torment inflicted on new recruits.
For weeks, I had watched David from afar, waiting
for the right moment to reveal myself. It was fear
that kept me removed, silent. If he rejected me
after all I had survived to find him, I knew life's worth
would vanish like vapor. One day, an announcement—
the fort would host a dance at the post. Yes, this was it,
the special occasion I had been waiting for. At the dance,
I would meet him face to face, just as we had on that first
night when he signed my dance card, assigned my fate.

Dance Partners

Ft. Gibson was the center for society in the county,
which included Cherokee Nation, peopled with those
forced to these lands years before. I had heard rumors
about the charms of the Cherokee maidens, how many
had married soldiers, even officers, producing mixed
children who did not face the disgrace that would surely
have followed them in another place, one more civilized.
And there would also be the young women who had risked
the riverboats to connect with soldiers, some they had never
met but who were friends of friends, brothers, cousins.
All day, I practiced what I would do and say. Of course,
I would still be disguised as Thomas. There was no way
to don a dress, to transform, as in the Cinderella story,
to a different person. I would wait for him to be alone,
and I would draw near. Touching him on the sleeve,
I would feel him bristle for a moment at the audacity,
before removing my hat, moving my eyes to his face,
and in that moment, he would at last know the truth.
As evening fell, the sound of music filled the prairie—
fiddles, guitars, harmonicas. David made his way
into the circle of guests, shaking hands, smiling.
When he finally found a corner removed from clamor,
I rose and started toward him, my heart pumping
so hard that I was reminded of Pleas' clopping hooves.
Just a few feet away, I saw him look up, and a spark
of recognition, of delight, crossed his sunbaked face.
In front of him, pulling him to his feet, was a Cherokee
girl, nearly half my age, her hair streaming, gleaming
crow-like in the candlelight. I watched them dance
until I felt heaving that started at my core, and I raced
to the door, staggered back to a barren barracks.

Determination

For the first few days following the dance, trance-
like, I went through my days, like one of the mediums
who used to sit at the head of my mother's séance
tables, wearing glassy, unseeing eyes. Only the drills
kept me moving when I wanted to curl up on my cot
and will myself to die. But I still had hope, a small
burning ember that I could not extinguish. It was only
a dance, I told myself, more determined than ever
to let David know that I still loved him, still desired
to marry him. I would live wherever he wished. My tasks
at the camp varied from day to day—baking, feeding
the mules, tending the horses. But I was determined
to be put on patrol duty. David spent a great deal
of time outside the fort, keeping the peace among
the different groups of people living nearby. If only
I could meet him away from the stockade, I felt
the feelings we had shared would spark again,
and that tiny ember could be rekindled to a blaze.

Routine

Each evening, after supper, I watched David
mount his horse and disappear between the gates
that guarded our garrison. At the end of each day,
drums sounded retreat, followed by a single gun-
shot, and the ceremony of lowering the flag
as sunset bled red and orange against prairie sky.
At nine o'clock, the roll of the drum and shrill
notes of a fife warned stragglers to take their places
inside the palisades before the great gates drew
closed, shutting them out. Next, the playing of taps—
as lonely as the sound of coyotes that answered—
then only darkness, stillness. Each evening, as others
took part in diversions, I sat waiting for David's
return. His reappearance grew later and later,
his horse trotting between the gates just as they
swung secure. Imagine my joy when I learned
that I would be on patrol for a week. For seven
days I would have the freedom to roam outside
the walls, to follow David's path, to summon
the courage to show my face, to face him at last.

Patrolling

The first couple days did not go as planned on patrol,
and I lost sight of him when I held back, not wanting
him to know that I was following, longing to talk
to him alone. But on the third day, hiding behind
rocks and trees, I watched as he stopped at various
cabins built by the Cherokees. They greeted him,
like an old friend, children clinging to his hands,
giggling as he swung them around. I felt my heart
sink to think that by now I could have had his child,
his own son might have one day begged for one
more twirl. Or a little girl with chestnut hair might
have wrapped her arms around his neck, instead
of these children, going through his pockets, looking
for treats. His last stop was at a log door that opened
before he could knock. Out stepped the same girl
who had asked him to dance. She moved like a doe,
stepping softly with slender ankles, and she cocked
her head to one side as if listening, even when he
did not speak. They walked together along a path
filled with fallen leaves, and I remembered our first
stroll, chaperoned by my sister. Always accompanied,
we never had the chance to be totally alone. Now
here he was with a much younger girl, walking
so closely together their arms touched, and I clutched
my fist to my mouth when I saw him take her hand,
raise it to his lips, and plant a kiss on her gloveless palm.

Lies I Told Myself

That night, I cried silently in the darkness, while snores
filled the air in the barracks. I, who had spent my life
learning the fine art of being a lady, who had studied
ancient history and literature, who had spent countless
hours painting and needlepointing, who had graduated
charm school, was being outcharmed by someone wild,
untamed in my eyes. What could she offer an officer
that I could not? She would never know the proper
fork to use for oysters, the placement of dinner napkins.
She was simply a poor substitute since David thought
I was still in Boston. He could never truly be serious
about anyone of her caliber. This girl with hair, blue-
black as a rook, was simply an amusement, a way
to pass the day. All I had to do was announce myself,
and any thought of this Cherokee girl would waft away
like smoke from a campfire. I was resolved to reveal
myself the next day, and I finally fell asleep clutching
to my chest the groom's gift that kept time with my heart.

Coward

I did not reveal myself as I had promised. Day
after day, even when I was assigned other tasks,
I managed to find my way to the cabin where
Woya—for that was her name—lived. I asked
one of the older soldiers who spent his time
in the kitchen what the word meant, and he said
it was Cherokee for *dove*. Even her name felt
like a slap, for my own name was a meaningless
cluster of letters strung together like pearls
made of paste. Week after week, David made
his way to her cabin home, and with each visit,
both became braver in the way they touched
until the time came when he lifted her upward,
her tiny feet dangling, and he kissed her lips
so deeply that I thought I would die in my hiding
place. Without thinking, I stumbled away, headed
toward the river which had brought me to this place
with promises that had now been dashed. I dashed
into the water, cold but not flowing swiftly. I prayed
to be taken away, to drown in these waters, to drift
as far as possible. But I did not sink, did not drown,
and the human desire to live buoyed me back to shore.

The Final Visit

The seasons changed. Late September settled
in, altering the landscape, but not my obsession.
I continued to follow the couple, to observe
their rituals as if I were watching a play staged
outside. But the day came when David approached
the cozy cabin with its wreath of chimney smoke,
and Woya spoke to him at the door, before pulling
him inside. There was a window on the side,
and I am ashamed to say that I could not turn aside,
could not stop watching the players reciting lines,
going through their scripted motions. First, she gave
him something steaming in a cup, and when done,
she took it from him. Her hair was loose and long,
tumbling, sparking from the firelight. Then slowly
she removed his coat, lifted his shirt over his head,
revealing his broad chest. In turn, he lifted her dress
over her head, smoothing down her hair. The next
moment, he was standing, wearing nothing, then
in one swift movement, he swept her from her feet
and laid her on a bed covered with a quilt. Guilt
did not enter my mind as I watched what should
have been mine, mine, mine.

The Strongest

There are people, who if asked, would answer
that the strongest emotion a person can feel
is love, while another will argue that it is hate.
But I know now it is neither. I could not hate
the man I loved to my core, not even knowing
I had been betrayed by his needs. No, I learned
the strongest emotion is loss because it waits
in its lair, growing and growing over time,
developing teeth that gnaw away from inside,
consuming the person who nurtured it, fed it
with the false hope of reclamation. Love
and hate and rage fill a person to overflowing,
but loss leaves a hollowness, an empty, echoing
cave of nothingness. My losses were calling
out to me, reverberating, haunting and taunting,
as I finally moved away from the window. My
family, my fortune, my friends. My losses
were resounding inside my head as I hid behind
the rocky outcropping, waiting for David to ride
by. I was not filled with love or hate or rage
as I cocked the pistol, pulled the trigger, heard
the blast resonate, saw a giant red rose bloom
on his uniformed chest. There was only loss.

Regret

The moment I saw David fall from his horse,
the spell was broken. Whatever mania had seized
my mind ceased to be, and I sent a shriek upward,
a howl to the heavens when I realized my actions.
I ran to him, and in that moment, when our eyes locked,
a look of recognition, a slight twitch of his brow,
a question, before his lids shut. I thought him dead,
and so I stumbled back to my horse and rode hard
back to the barracks. I cannot explain the turmoil
roiling in my mind and body. How could I have
killed the only man I had ever loved, would ever
love? As evening settled around the camp, word
spread that David had not returned. The time
to close the gates was close at hand, and never
had he been late. A search party quickly assembled,
and my stomach lurched as I looked on, knowing
what they would find. Time meant nothing to me,
but they finally returned with a body draping
a horse. There was shouting for a medic. David
had been shot but was alive. My knees collapsed
beneath me, and kneeling, I could only pray
for his survival. I did not deserve forgiveness.

Hope Dies

For several days, David lay in a state
of slumber, never opening his eyes.
A fever had sent his body into tremors,
and I volunteered to help the doctor
draw cool water from the well, to bathe
David's brow and arms. It was a chance
to truly look at him once again, not a glance
from afar. Time and climate had left traces
on his face, but he was still the most splendid
man I had ever met. He continued to linger,
my fingers lacing with his when nobody
was near. Then one morning, I reported
and found his bunk empty. The doctor called
it a blessing that he had finally been taken
during the night, no longer suffering. Numb,
I stumbled from the hospital. The word
grief comes from the Latin *gravare,*
meaning *to make heavy,* and my feet,
at that moment, felt too heavy to lift,
my soul too weighted to carry its burden.

Investigation

I was in such a state that it never occurred to me
that an investigation would take place. Each day,
I told myself that I would go to my commanding
officer, admit my guilt, face the firing squad
if necessary. But every morning, I rose to rose-
colored skies and golden trees, now that October
had pushed September from the calendar. Weeks
passed, and no suspects were arrested. Rumors
spread that David's kindness to the Cherokees
had developed into something more, causing
conflict with some who resented a white man's
intrusion. The official report was released at last,
near the last of the month. An unknown Indian,
no doubt drunken, had shot David with a pistol
supplied by the Army during the Civil War.
Since there were no witnesses, no charges
would be filed, no justice for the lieutenant,
whose life became a cautionary tale. Absolution
was not for the officers to give, though. No
person living on earth could exonerate me.

The Weight of Guilt

I do not know why I stayed. My reason for being
at the fort, my reason for being, was buried
beneath Indian Territory soil. I could desert,
return to the life I had known, and no one
would ever be able to find Private Thomas.
He would have simply vanished like one
of the haints the boys from Arkansas talked
about as we worked the riverboats. But
I carried the guilt of David's death, wrapped
my arms around it as if it were his child
I had carried, birthed, and now nurtured.
And just as a baby grows each day, develops
its own life, so my guilt sprouted, matured
into its own being. Where loss had left
a hollow spot, guilt now dwelled, filling
me with a constant hunger to tell the truth,
to relieve myself of this monstrous offspring.

Visitation

I began to visit David's grave each evening,
sometimes lying prone in hopes my own body
could dissolve into the soil, join him in his bed
for eternity. One day I brought with me a gift,
the watch inscribed with the promise of timeless
love, and dug a hole, letting the chain snake
from my fingers to join the gold timepiece. Peace
still eluded me, and I wept each time I stepped
near his tombstone. As chilly November winds
wove their way through the cemetery, I vowed
to visit the camp chaplain. I had never been
a great believer, relegating religion to the elderly
women who sat in the front row of our church,
who brought fresh flowers from their gardens
to adorn the altar, paying for a place in heaven.
But now I feared for my immortal soul, sobbed
myself awake at night with visions of boiling
blood and brimstone. It was my intent to repent.

The Chaplain

It took several days to find the chaplain alone
inside the church. He seemed surprised to see me
since I had not been a regular attendee. I closed
the door, fixed the inside latch, and I did catch
a flicker of fear or uncertainty in his smooth face.
Without waiting for him to ask what I needed,
I stood before him, removed my cap, opened
my shirt to show the bindings. He stumbled
back as the words tumbled from my mouth,
the story of falling in love, of following
all the way by carriage and rail and river.
Then I confessed to being not only a woman
but a murderess, the worst kind, a cowardly
sort who cowered behind a rock and shot
the only man I had ever loved because his love
for me was not strong enough to stand the test
of time and place. I buried my face inside
my hands, fell to my knees, pleading for relief.
He finally knelt beside me, placed his hand
on top of my head, and asked God Almighty
to forgive me for my grievous transgressions.
Then he held me as we sat on the floor, rocking
as if I were a child who had broken an heirloom
and needed reassurance that all would be well.
And I knew, even if he could, he would never tell.

The Last New Year

I would like to say that confession cleansed
my soul, but it did not. Sharing my guilt,
instead of cutting it in half, only seemed
to multiply my misery. Christmas, a time
that had held so many warm memories,
came and went, but I found no joy in a holiday
that would only remind me of the Dickens
Christmas I had shared with David. Ignoring
cold and snow squalls that swept the prairie,
I went each night to his grave, praying, hoping
his ghost would appear to me, appease me.
But he was silent, his voice muffled beneath
the drifts. On New Year's Eve, I made my way
to his grave once again. I would stay with him
throughout the night, welcome in a new year
he would never see. My tears felt like daggers
as cold caught them on my cheeks. I wrapped
my arms around his headstone and let ice
seep into my marrow. And, finally, I slept.

Discovery

I was stirred from slumber by shouting, jostling,
as I was hoisted onto a horse. I could not open
my eyes or speak, and I thought I might be dead,
but instead, I heard someone say my heartbeat
was slow, breathing shallow, so I knew I lived.
Soldiers took me to the hospital, and I tried
to struggle, knowing if they opened my shirt,
they would learn my truth. I heard the chaplain
say something to the doctor who cursed, cut
away my ice-encrusted clothes, and wrapped
my body, now belonging to a woman, in blankets.
I could hear the chaplain praying for my soul,
the doctor's commands to let him work in peace.
He barked orders for broth and elixirs, both poured
down my throat, unable to swallow on my own.
Later that day, the chills began, and I shivered
until I thought my teeth might crack. Heat
scorched my skin, and I dreamt I had landed
in Hell, tortured by infernal fires. For a full
week, I fought against the unbeatable foe.

My Death (January 7, 1870)

I stood outside my body and watched the doctor
wipe his eyes as he gently laid my arm back
onto the blanket. He signaled to the chaplain
who had been dozing in a corner, and he took
my hand into his own as if trying to warm it,
then recited the Psalm about green pastures
and still waters. When he reached the part
about walking through the valley of the shadow
of death, I knew I had left my body behind.
There would be no more need for a disguise.
No longer would I feel the cold or heat,
the pangs of hunger or gnawing of thirst.
I thought that all of the desires of human
flesh would diminish, all memories of love
and hate would fade to nothingness, vapor.
But this was not to be my fate.

Legend

I never meant to be a legend . . . but then again
there were so many things I never meant to become—
a jilted bride, a cabin boy, a soldier, a murderess.
My punishment was not to burn in everlasting
blazes but rather to smolder with the fire of passion
throughout the decades, never ceasing to desire.
The soldiers who served with me, stunned to learn
that I was a woman, to hear of the hardships I faced
to follow love—only to learn of the fickle nature
of a man's heart—vowed to keep my memory alive,
to erect a stone in the same circle as war heroes
and their wives. Sometimes, even after a century,
two score and ten years more, there are those
who claim to see me, lying prone on my lover's
grave, still dressed in my Private Thomas uniform,
while others catch a glimpse of the girl I had been,
glorious in my wedding gown, still awaiting vows.
And always they say I weep. Yes, I weep—
in sorrow but also in gratitude that I continue to live
in the imaginations of so many. Never would I
have dreamt that my name—*Vivia*—engraved in white
marble stone, would still float from the throats of the living,
like seeds from Oklahoma prairie milkweed.

About the Author

Linda Neal Reising, a native of Oklahoma and citizen of the Cherokee Nation, has been published in numerous journals, including *The Southern Indiana Review, The Comstock Review,* and *Nimrod.* Reising's work has also appeared in a number of anthologies, including *Fruitflesh: Seeds of Inspiration for Women Who Write* (Harper/Collins), *And Know This Place: Poetry of Indiana* (Indiana Historical Society Press), and *Let Me Say This: A Dolly Parton Anthology (Madville Press).* She was named the winner of the 2012 Writer's Digest Poetry Competition, and her work has been nominated for a Pushcart Prize three times. Her chapbook, *Re-Writing Family History* (Finishing Line Press), was a finalist for the 2015 Oklahoma Book Award, as well as winner of the 2015 Oklahoma Writers' Federation Poetry Book Prize. *The Keeping* (Finishing Line Press), her first full-length book of poetry, won the 2020 Kops-Fetherling Phoenix Award for Outstanding New Voice in Poetry and the 2021 Human Relations Indie Book Awards. Her second full-length book, *Stone Roses* (Kelsay Books), was a finalist for the 2022 WILLA Award, the WWA Spur Awards, and the Oklahoma Book Award, as well as winning the Eric Hoffer Award and the Western Heritage Wrangler Award.